Vision Pages

A vision journal for
imagining your dreams to life

Barbara Jacksha

Cooper Brandberg
Publishing

Published by Cooper Brandberg Publishing in 2017
First edition; First printing

Design and writing @ 2017 Barbara Jacksha
www.barbarajacksha.com

Cover background artwork @Evannovostro/Shutterstock
Cover and interior artwork @ Tatyana Okhitina/Shutterstock

ISBN 978-0-9987121-0-9

Dedication

For all of you rediscovering

that the greatest, grandest,

most powerful visions of all

are the ones you carry

within you

"As you imagine and visualize and verbalize
your new story, in time you will believe the
new story, and when that happens,
the evidence will flow swiftly into your experience."

~ Esther Hicks ~

Welcome to Your Vision Pages

Imagination is a powerful tool. We all have it, yet we rarely tap its full potential. Writing vision pages changes that. Vision pages help you dust off your imagination and play with it as the immense, exciting, creative force it is.

Writing vision pages is like creating a vision board, but it goes far beyond the limiting images and words of others. Writing about your dreams and desires with your own hands, in your own words, helps you tap into your inner vision, imagination and power in a way that is uniquely you!

For decades I wrote Morning Pages, a wonderful freewriting process birthed by the author Julia Cameron. At a certain point I longed to sharpen my focus. As a writer, I wanted to expand my creative process and manifest my passions and ideas. I wanted to create from deeply held visions of everything I wanted in every area of life: health, money, relationships, etc.

Out of those longings, vision pages were born. Every morning I began writing about what I wanted to have, experience, be and feel. The more I wrote, the clearer I got about what I truly desired. And the more I saw changes emerge in my life that echoed what I'd been writing in my journal. I quickly realized the creative power of writing vision pages, a process fueled largely by imagination.

As the months of writing vision pages went by, I saw four distinct stages to the practice emerge: writing, feeling, choosing and creating. I'll explain these on the next few pages. Keep them in mind as you play with your own vision pages and experience their power for yourself.

Writing vision pages is an amazing adventure. Relax and have fun imagining your dreams to life!

With love and gratitude,

Barbara

Writing Your Vision Pages

Write it!

The first step to writing vision pages is simple. Write about what you want! It doesn't matter what your desire is. It can be a physical thing, a passion or vocation, a relationship, an inner quality like patience, or an experience of heart-expanding joy.

It's important to claim your desires. Own them. In life we often have a hard time claiming what we want or even acknowledging our desires to ourselves. We often deny what we want thinking it's too much, we're not worthy, it's selfish, etc. Forget all those objections here. In your journal you have full permission and authority to name and claim and play with everything you desire!

Writing your desires by hand is the very tactile process of moving your dreams from your heart and mind to the physical page of your journal. Once written, the words representing your desires are literally here in the world. You can see the words. You can touch them. They're physical things seeded here in your everyday life. And from these seeds, so many wonderful things can grow.

I recommend writing in the present tense, as though you already have what you desire. By writing this way you're creating and telling a new story that already has a happy ending. Let it be the best, most wonderful story you can tell. Let it be exciting and outrageously fun. Let your imagination loose and let the new story resonate within you.

Sensory details help the story come alive and help your dreams feel and become more real to you. If you desire a new house, for example, write and describe how the house looks from the street, how the rooms look, what the view is from the front window. Imagine and feel the texture of the wall and the soft way the carpeting cushions your feet. Hear the swish of curtains as you open them for the first time. Smell your first dinner in the new house cooking in the kitchen. Let yourself sink fully into the sensory experience as you write. Make it seem as real as you can, which will lead you into the next step.

Writing Your Vision Pages

Feel it!

While you imagine and write about what you desire, let the feelings come through. What does it feel like to now have what you desire? Going back to our house example, how does living in that new house feel? Do you feel a lovely rootedness, a sense of expansion or excitement, or simply joy? It doesn't matter what the feelings are as long as they feel good! Let these good feelings and thoughts become part of the story you tell as you write.

Let the feelings of having what you want come in through your writing as fully as you can. Why? First of all, good feelings feel delicious, don't they? In addition, these feelings can be even more important than the physical thing you desire. Isn't it really the feelings you're after? So often we think we want something like a house just for the house itself. But most of the time, we want something because we expect it will make us feel good. When you imagine and include feelings in your vision pages, they help you get very clear about the deeper feelings you really want, feelings that manifest as your outer desires. Maybe that new house is only the surface expression of your desire to feel centered and grounded in your life. Once you uncover and get clear about these feelings, you can open more fully to all the other marvelous and surprising ways those feelings can come to you.

One great result of writing vision pages is that you realize you don't have to wait for what you desire to physically manifest in the world. You can have and experience the feelings you desire right now. Right in your vision pages. Feel them, enjoy them, play with them. Celebrate that you don't need the new house to appear in order to enjoy the feelings of having it. And in turn these experiences of good feelings will attract even more of what you desire.

Every time you feel good, even in writing vision pages, it signals your body and your brain. They like to feel good too! The more you write vision pages and repeat the sensations, the more the feelings start to feel normal and highly desirable to both your body and brain. Trust that your subconscious will start looking for ways to bring more of those feelings in. Maybe it will be through the house of your dreams, or maybe the feelings will come in other ways that are even more spectacular.

When you write vision pages, don't worry about how anything will show up in your physical world. Just play with your desires and experience how they make you feel. Trust that the more you play in the realm of good feelings, the more the Universe will bring those feelings to you!

Writing Your Vision Pages

Choose it!

In many visualization techniques, choice is the missing piece. In your vision pages, when you write something that feels exciting and good, choose it. Declare your intent to have, be, do or experience more of THAT. Choosing is incredibly powerful. Choosing reminds you that you are in charge. And choosing activates all within you that can support your choices.

Write your choices in your vision pages. This anchors your choices into the physical world, on paper, just as you anchor the desires and feelings you write about.

As you write your vision pages, you have free rein to choose anything, any feeling or experience or vision, you want. Every new choice is a message to the Universe about what you want to have, be, feel or experience. Choose a new thing every day, or choose the same things, playfully choosing them in different ways, to solidify them within you as your new reality.

You can even use your *Vision Pages* journal to make lists of choices. Write down choices that you're aware of. Write down choices that simply show up in the moment, choices that flow without your conscious thought. You can start each line with the same phrase:

I choose _____

I choose _____

I choose _____

I choose _____

I choose _____

I choose _____

You get the idea. The powerful, open-hearted feeling of doing this might surprise you.

Writing Your Vision Pages

Create it!

This final step comes after you've written your vision pages and set the stage for new creations and experiences to emerge in your life. How do you move into creating? In a myriad of ways, but there are two fundamental parts of the creation process.

First is the receiving and allowing. When you've put your intent in motion through writing, feeling and choosing, the Universe and your subconscious all go to work. From a Law of Attraction standpoint, writing vision pages puts you into greater and greater alignment with the vibration of all the things, feelings, situations and experiences you desire, drawing them naturally to you.

Let it become a fun game to watch and see what shows up in life for you to receive. Who calls out of the blue with the help you need? Which article appears on Facebook giving you the perfect information at the perfect time? Sometimes what shows up arrives with trumpets blaring, but often it is subtle. So keep your eyes open.

It's wonderful when the Universe brings us something that fulfills our desires without our needing to do anything. At other times, however, we're called to take inspired action.

Inspired action is sometimes called aligned action, divine action or right action. Whatever the term, it means the kind of action we take when we recognize that an opportunity to act is aligned with who we are and what we truly desire. These opportunities feel exciting and full of potential. They may also feel a little unnerving because inspired action often nudges us to open a bit more, take more risk and step beyond our comfort zones. If fear comes up, remember what you wrote in your vision pages. Remember the wonderful feelings you felt and all the delightful choices you made. Let these support you and help you take the inspired action that will help manifest what you desire.

Inspired action also comes back to paying attention. What do you feel compelled to do? Who do you want to speak with? What do you feel you need to begin? Or end? When you feel the alignment, when you feel how perfect the action is for all that you've been writing, feeling and choosing, it's a simple matter of taking action and claiming the opportunity for yourself. For your joy and the fulfillment of your desires here in the physical world.

Vision Pages as a Practice

You can write vision pages as often as you like. A frequent practice of writing, feeling and choosing your desires can help speed up your ability to create them. Writing vision pages also feels good, so why not invite more good feelings into your days? Why not get used to living and playing in the realm where you can make your dreams come true? A daily practice is wonderful, but only you know what's best for you. If daily writing is too much, then write on whatever schedule feels good.

You can write vision pages for five minutes or an hour. I generally write until I feel finished, until I feel and embody the emotional state I desire. That can take three pages or five lines. Writing vision pages isn't about quantity. Use the way you feel as your guide. Some days, all it takes is a sentence or two to click back into the feeling of having what you desire. If that happens, celebrate the feeling in your journal and choose it until you feel the choice alive within you.

When you write during the day is also up to you. First thing in the morning is a great time, for it helps you start your day in an aligned, energized way. Writing in the evenings or before bed lets you set your desires in motion before entering into a powerful dream state. The middle of the day is helpful as well, especially when you want to shift your mood or redirect your focus.

Above all, let writing vision pages be easy and fun. Do them in whatever way feels good for you in the moment. Let yourself go and let yourself dream big! You deserve it!

"Imagination is the beginning of creation.
You imagine what you desire,
you will what you imagine,
and at last you create what you will."

George Bernard Shaw

Your Turn to Play!

The rest of the book is yours to play with. Make it your own. Follow the lines or write diagonally across the page. Doodle, add stickers, tuck love notes to yourself between the pages. Have fun with it!

Special areas are sprinkled throughout. You can play with the spaces the way I suggest below or use them in your own perfect ways.

 A page with a heart gives you space to jot a message from your heart, the source of your greatest imagination. Or give yourself a message of love and encouragement. You're doing great!

 A page with fireworks gives you space to celebrate. What feels great? What wonderful thing has shown up in your life? Or congratulate yourself for giving your visions, desires and imagination a much higher priority in your life!

 A page with a gift box gives you space to record the gifts you're opening: within yourself, within your life, within your vision pages. You don't need to think long and hard about what the gift is, just let the knowing flow into you!

"Extraordinary people visualize not what is possible or
probable, but rather what is impossible.

And by visualizing the impossible,
they begin to see it as possible."

~ Cherie Carter-Scott ~

Write it ~ Feel it ~ Choose it ~ Create it!

Write it ~ Feel it ~ Choose it ~ Create it!

Write it ~ Feel it ~ Choose it ~ Create it!

Write it ~ Feel it ~ Choose it ~ Create it!

Write it ~ Feel it ~ Choose it ~ Create it!

Write it ~ Feel it ~ Choose it ~ Create it!

Write it ~ Feel it ~ Choose it ~ Create it!

Write it ~ Feel it ~ Choose it ~ Create it!

Write it ~ Feel it ~ Choose it ~ Create it!

Write it ~ Feel it ~ Choose it ~ Create it!

Write it ~ Feel it ~ Choose it ~ Create it!

Write it ~ Feel it ~ Choose it ~ Create it!

Write it ~ Feel it ~ Choose it ~ Create it!

Write it ~ Feel it ~ Choose it ~ Create it!

Write it ~ Feel it ~ Choose it ~ Create it!

Write it ~ Feel it ~ Choose it ~ Create it!

Write it ~ Feel it ~ Choose it ~ Create it!

Write it ~ Feel it ~ Choose it ~ Create it!

Write it ~ Feel it ~ Choose it ~ Create it!

Write it ~ Feel it ~ Choose it ~ Create it!

Write it ~ Feel it ~ Choose it ~ Create it!

Write it ~ Feel it ~ Choose it ~ Create it!

Write it ~ Feel it ~ Choose it ~ Create it!

Write it ~ Feel it ~ Choose it ~ Create it!

Write it ~ Feel it ~ Choose it ~ Create it!

Write it ~ Feel it ~ Choose it ~ Create it!

Write it ~ Feel it ~ Choose it ~ Create it!

Write it ~ Feel it ~ Choose it ~ Create it!

Write it ~ Feel it ~ Choose it ~ Create it!

Write it ~ Feel it ~ Choose it ~ Create it!

Write it ~ Feel it ~ Choose it ~ Create it!

Write it ~ Feel it ~ Choose it ~ Create it!

Write it ~ Feel it ~ Choose it ~ Create it!

Write it ~ Feel it ~ Choose it ~ Create it!

Write it ~ Feel it ~ Choose it ~ Create it!

Write it ~ Feel it ~ Choose it ~ Create it!

Write it ~ Feel it ~ Choose it ~ Create it!

Write it ~ Feel it ~ Choose it ~ Create it!

Write it ~ Feel it ~ Choose it ~ Create it!

Write it ~ Feel it ~ Choose it ~ Create it!

Write it ~ Feel it ~ Choose it ~ Create it!

Write it ~ Feel it ~ Choose it ~ Create it!

Write it ~ Feel it ~ Choose it ~ Create it!

Write it ~ Feel it ~ Choose it ~ Create it!

Write it ~ Feel it ~ Choose it ~ Create it!

Write it ~ Feel it ~ Choose it ~ Create it!

Write it ~ Feel it ~ Choose it ~ Create it!

Write it ~ Feel it ~ Choose it ~ Create it!

Write it ~ Feel it ~ Choose it ~ Create it!

Write it ~ Feel it ~ Choose it ~ Create it!

Write it ~ Feel it ~ Choose it ~ Create it!

Write it ~ Feel it ~ Choose it ~ Create it!

Write it ~ Feel it ~ Choose it ~ Create it!

Write it ~ Feel it ~ Choose it ~ Create it!

Write it ~ Feel it ~ Choose it ~ Create it!

Write it ~ Feel it ~ Choose it ~ Create it!

Write it ~ Feel it ~ Choose it ~ Create it!

Write it ~ Feel it ~ Choose it ~ Create it!

Write it ~ Feel it ~ Choose it ~ Create it!

Write it ~ Feel it ~ Choose it ~ Create it!

Write it ~ Feel it ~ Choose it ~ Create it!

Write it ~ Feel it ~ Choose it ~ Create it!

Write it ~ Feel it ~ Choose it ~ Create it!

Write it ~ Feel it ~ Choose it ~ Create it!

Write it ~ Feel it ~ Choose it ~ Create it!

Write it ~ Feel it ~ Choose it ~ Create it!

Write it ~ Feel it ~ Choose it ~ Create it!

Write it ~ Feel it ~ Choose it ~ Create it!

Write it ~ Feel it ~ Choose it ~ Create it!

Write it ~ Feel it ~ Choose it ~ Create it!

Write it ~ Feel it ~ Choose it ~ Create it!

Write it ~ Feel it ~ Choose it ~ Create it!

Write it ~ Feel it ~ Choose it ~ Create it!

Write it ~ Feel it ~ Choose it ~ Create it!

Write it ~ Feel it ~ Choose it ~ Create it!

Write it ~ Feel it ~ Choose it ~ Create it!

Write it ~ Feel it ~ Choose it ~ Create it!

Write it ~ Feel it ~ Choose it ~ Create it!

Write it ~ Feel it ~ Choose it ~ Create it!

Write it ~ Feel it ~ Choose it ~ Create it!

Write it ~ Feel it ~ Choose it ~ Create it!

Write it ~ Feel it ~ Choose it ~ Create it!

Write it ~ Feel it ~ Choose it ~ Create it!

Write it ~ Feel it ~ Choose it ~ Create it!

Write it ~ Feel it ~ Choose it ~ Create it!

Write it ~ Feel it ~ Choose it ~ Create it!

Write it ~ Feel it ~ Choose it ~ Create it!

Write it ~ Feel it ~ Choose it ~ Create it!

Write it ~ Feel it ~ Choose it ~ Create it!

Write it ~ Feel it ~ Choose it ~ Create it!

Write it ~ Feel it ~ Choose it ~ Create it!

Write it ~ Feel it ~ Choose it ~ Create it!

Write it ~ Feel it ~ Choose it ~ Create it!

Write it ~ Feel it ~ Choose it ~ Create it!

Write it ~ Feel it ~ Choose it ~ Create it!

Write it ~ Feel it ~ Choose it ~ Create it!

Write it ~ Feel it ~ Choose it ~ Create it!

Write it ~ Feel it ~ Choose it ~ Create it!

Write it ~ Feel it ~ Choose it ~ Create it!

Write it ~ Feel it ~ Choose it ~ Create it!

Write it ~ Feel it ~ Choose it ~ Create it!

Write it ~ Feel it ~ Choose it ~ Create it!

Write it ~ Feel it ~ Choose it ~ Create it!

Write it ~ Feel it ~ Choose it ~ Create it!

Write it ~ Feel it ~ Choose it ~ Create it!

Write it ~ Feel it ~ Choose it ~ Create it!

Write it ~ Feel it ~ Choose it ~ Create it!

Write it ~ Feel it ~ Choose it ~ Create it!

Write it ~ Feel it ~ Choose it ~ Create it!

Write it ~ Feel it ~ Choose it ~ Create it!

Write it ~ Feel it ~ Choose it ~ Create it!

Write it ~ Feel it ~ Choose it ~ Create it!

Write it ~ Feel it ~ Choose it ~ Create it!

Write it ~ Feel it ~ Choose it ~ Create it!

Write it ~ Feel it ~ Choose it ~ Create it!

Write it ~ Feel it ~ Choose it ~ Create it!

Write it ~ Feel it ~ Choose it ~ Create it!

Write it ~ Feel it ~ Choose it ~ Create it!

Write it ~ Feel it ~ Choose it ~ Create it!

Write it ~ Feel it ~ Choose it ~ Create it!

~ extra page for doodles or drawings ~

~ extra page for doodles or drawings ~

~ extra page for doodles or drawings ~

~ extra page for doodles or drawings ~

~ extra page for doodles or drawings ~

CPSIA information can be obtained
at www.ICGtesting.com
Printed in the USA
LVHW101015271118
598395LV00003B/219/P